The Custom of Marrying Cousins

کزنوں سے شادی کرنے کا رواج

by Nazira Ahmed

Text copyright © Nazira Ahmed 1999
Illustrations: Jane Dodds
Book design and artwork: David Andrassy
Urdu translation: Nasreem Saleemi
Urdu typesetting: The Translation and Interpretation Service,
Manchester City Council
Editor: Yasmin Alam

Published and distributed by Gatehouse Books Ltd.,
Hulme Adult Education Centre, Stretford Road, Manchester M15 5FQ

Printed by RAP Ltd., Rochdale.

ISBN 0 906 253 90 X

British Library cataloguing in publication data:
A catalogue record for this book is available from the British Library

Many thanks to Michaela Salmon, tutor at Plymouth Grove Adult Education
Centre, for encouraging her ESOL students to write, and contributing to the
selection process. Many thanks also to piloting groups composed of ESOL
students organised by Nan Jackson, Co-ordinator of the Partnership Education
Project at Rochdale and and Lyn Carter, ESOL Team Leader at Huddersfield
Technical College. Mahbub and Aisha Mian, Marilyn Martin-Jones, Mustafa
Erdogdu and Shamshad Khan also gave generously of their time, providing
invaluable support and insights facilitating the editorial process.

Gatehouse is grateful for continued financial support from Manchester City
Council and North West Arts Board, and for financial assistance for the
development of the Asian Women's Writing and Publishing Project, from the
National Lottery Charities Board, Barrow-Cadbury Trust, Save and Prosper
Educational Trust, Kellogg's and Garfield Weston Foundation.

Our thanks for their ongoing support to Manchester Lifelong Learning.

Gatehouse is a member of The Federation of Worker Writers
& Community Publishers
Gatehouse Publishing Charity is a charity registered in England no. 1011042

supported by

north west arts board

NATIONAL
LOTTERY
CHARITIES
BOARD

What is Thalassaemia?

Thalassaemia is an inherited condition, affecting the blood. There are two types, thalassaemia minor and thalassaemia major.

If both parents have thalassaemia minor, then there is:

1) a 25% chance their child will not be affected at all
2) a 50% chance their child will get thalassaemia minor
3) a 25% chance their child will get thalassaemia major.

The child with thalassaemia major will be very anaemic and will need regular blood transfusions for the rest of its life.

Couples can find out if either or both of them have got thalassaemia minor, by having a special blood test. If you would like more information, or you or a family member want to have a blood test done, please see a doctor.

تھلیسیمیاء کیا ہے؟

تھلیسیمیاء ورثے میں ملنے والی ایک بیماری ہے جس کا اثر خون پر ہوتا ہے۔ اس کی دو اقسام ہیں؛ تھلیسیمیاء چھوٹا اور تھلیسیمیاء بڑا۔

اگر والدین کو تھلیسیمیاء چھوٹا ہو تو:

25 فیصد اس بات کا امکان ہوتا ہے کہ یہ بیماری ان کے بچوں پر اثرانداز نہیں ہوگی۔

50 فیصد اس بات کا امکان ہوتا ہے کہ ان کے بچوں کو چھوٹا تھلیسیمیاء ہو سکتا ہے۔

اور 25 فیصد اس بات کا امکان ہوتا ہے کہ ان کے بچوں کو تھلیسیمیاء بڑا ہو۔

وہ بچہ جس کو تھلیسیمیاء بڑا ہو تو اس کے خون میں سرخ ذرات کی کمی پیدا ہو جاتی ہے اور تا زندگی اس کو باقاعدگی سے خون لینا پڑے گا۔

اگر میاں بیوی چاہیں تو وہ خون کا ٹیسٹ کروا کر یہ جان سکتے ہیں کہ کیا ان میں تھلیسیمیاء چھوٹا ہے یا نہیں؛

اگر آپ یا آپ کے گھر کے کسی فرد کو اس بارے میں مزید معلومات درکار ہوں یا آپ خون کا ٹیسٹ کروانا چاہتے ہوں تو ڈاکٹر سے رابطہ کریں۔

Introduction

My name is Nazira Ahmed.
I grew up in Pakistan, in the city of Karachi.
I stopped going to school when I was nine years old.
I stopped because the teacher was bullying me.
She used to hit me a lot.
So I started playing truant.
No-one in my family knew.
I was too scared to tell anyone.
I would hide all day in the play area near the school.
This went on for months.
Anyway, when I failed my exams at the end of the year,
my parents said, "Oh, you are no good at school!"
They decided not to let me go to school any more.
They thought I was not clever enough.
But they did not know how many months of school
I missed because I was so scared of that horrible teacher.
Because of her, I learnt nothing and my life was ruined.
What I mean is, I did not learn to read and write
because of this teacher.
I wish I had told my parents about this teacher,
but at the time, I was too scared. So I kept quiet.
Now, I am going to English classes.
I am learning to read and write
and there is something important I have to say.
Thanks to Gatehouse for giving me the chance.

When I was sixteen years old,
I was married to my first cousin.
He lived in England.
I joined him in Manchester in 1985.

جب میری عمر سولہ سال کی ہوئی،
میری شادی میرے فسٹ کزن سے طے پائی ۔
وہ انگلینڈ میں رہتا تھا ۔
میں اُس کے پاس مانچسٹر میں 1985ء میں آئی ۔

2

We had three children.
Naima was ten years old
when she started feeling tired
all the time.
I took her to the doctor's
and some tests were done.
Then we got the sad news.
She had a blood disease
called thalassaemia.
We knew nothing about this disease.

3

ہمارے ہاں تین بچے پیدا ہوئے۔

نعیمہ دس سال کی تھی

جب وہ تمام وقت

تھکی تھکی رہنے لگی۔

میں اُسے ڈاکٹر کے پاس لے گئی

اور اُس کے کچھ ٹیسٹ ہوئے۔

تب ہمیں یہ افسوسناک خبر ملی کہ

اس کو خون کی بیماری ہے

جسے تھیلیسیمیاء کہتے ہیں۔

ہمیں اس مرض کے بارے میں کچھ معلوم نہیں تھا۔

4

The doctor told us
that she did not have
the serious type of the disease,
but if she married a person
with the same problem,
then their children might have
very serious health problems.

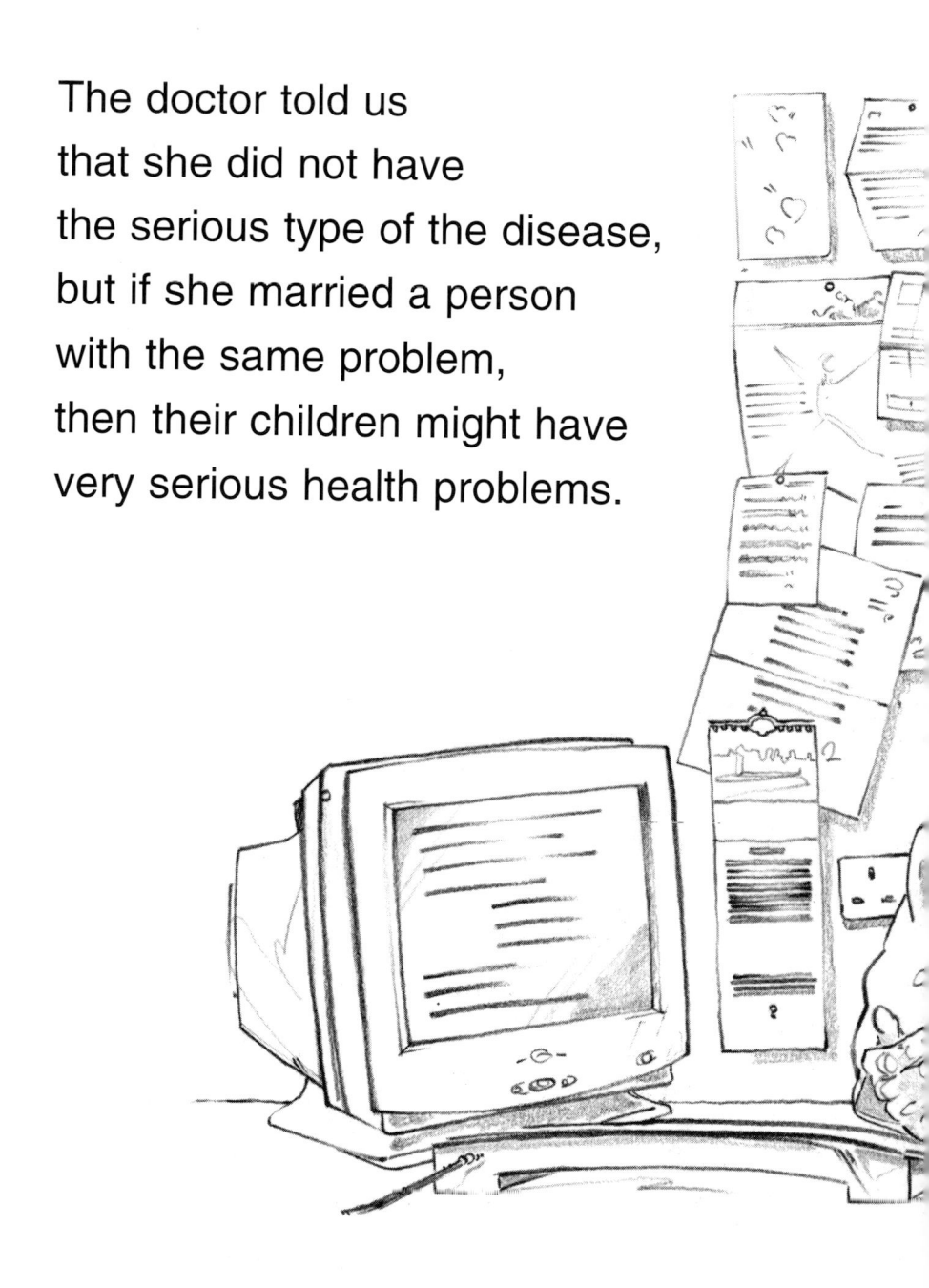

ڈاکٹر نے ہمیں بتایا
کہ اس قسم کی مرض
خطرناک قسم کی نہیں ہے
لیکن اگر اس نے شادی کسی ایسے شخص سے
کی جس کو یہی بیماری ہوئی
تو پھر ان کے بچوں کو تشویشناک بیماریاں
ہو سکتی ہیں۔

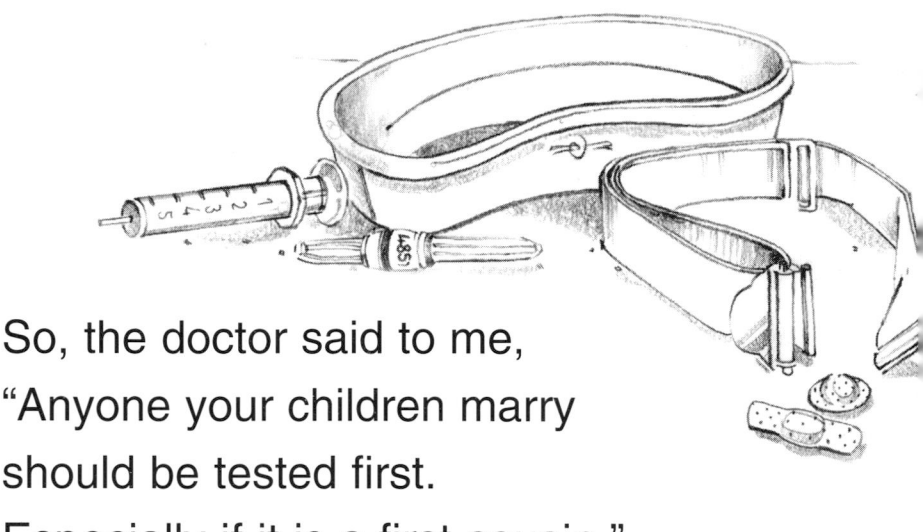

So, the doctor said to me,
"Anyone your children marry
should be tested first.
Especially if it is a first cousin."
So, my husband and I decided
not to have any more children.
We are very sad about our daughter.
We are sad that no-one told us
that there would be a high chance
of our children having health problems
because my husband and I
are first cousins.
This is true, especially if there have been
a lot of first cousin marriages
in your family in the past.

I still had not told my family
about the situation,
when one day, my mother phoned me
from Karachi. We chatted for a while
and I had a feeling
she was going to ask me
something important.

میں نے ابھی تک اپنے خاندان میں
کسی کو اپنے حالات کے متعلق نہیں بتایا تھا۔
جب ایک دن میری والدہ نے
کراچی سے فون کیا۔ ہماری بات چیت کے دوران
میں نے محسوس کیا
کہ وہ مجھ سے کچھ ضروری چیز
پوچھنا چاہتی ہیں۔

10

At last my mother reminded me
that my brother Saeed
has five daughters.
"Are you going to agree
to marry your sons to their cousins,
Saira and Seema?"
I said to my mother
I would talk it over with my husband
and then let her know.

آخر کار میری ماں نے مجھے یاد دلایا

کہ میرے بھائی سعید

کی پانچ بیٹیاں ہیں۔

"کیا تم رضامند ہو

کہ تمہارے بیٹوں کی شادی ان کی ماموں زاد

سائرہ اور سیماں سے طے ہو"۔

میں نے اپنی والدہ سے کہا

کہ میں اپنے خاوند سے بات کر کے

اُنہیں بتا دوُں گی۔

12

Of course, my husband and I
have been discussing
this custom of marrying cousins.
Sometimes people do it because
they feel their daughters are safer,
married within the family.
Sometimes it is to keep land together.

بے شک کزنوں سے شادی کا رواج

میرے اور میرے خاوند کے درمیان

زیرِ موضوع رہا ہے۔

کچھ لوگ اس لئے شادی خاندان میں کرتے ہیں

کیونکہ وہ سمجھتے ہیں کہ اُن کی بیٹیاں محفوظ رہیں گی۔

بعض دفعہ اس لئے کہ زمین اکٹھی رہے۔

14

Nowadays, it is often because
the family want to send
their offspring to the rich West.
Meanwhile, some families here
think a girl from "back home" will be
more obedient and more "respectable".
Some people marry their children
to their cousins, just because
that is the way it has always been done.
It is a sort of habit, passed on
from one generation to the next.

آجکل ایسا اس لئے کچھ خاندانوں میں ہوتا ہے

کیونکہ اکثر خاندان یہ چاہتے ہیں کہ ان کی اولاد

باہر کے امیر ملکوں میں جا سکے۔

تاہم، یہاں کے کچھ خاندان سمجھتے ہیں کہ

اپنے ملکوں سے لائی ہوئی لڑکی زیادہ فرمانبردار اور باادب ہو گی۔

بعض لوگ اپنے بچوں کی شادی ان کے کزنوں سے

صرف اس لئے کرتے ہیں کیونکہ ایسا ہمیشہ سے ہوتا آیا ہے،

ایک طرح سے یہ عادت ہے جو نسل در نسل منتقل ہوتی آئی ہے۔

16

My husband and I sat down one day
and looked at photos of
both sides of our family.
We began noticing how many of
our close and distant relatives
were having children born with health
problems. Many were disabled.
Some had died soon after birth.

میں نے اور میرے خاوند نے ایک دن بیٹھ کر
دونوں طرف کے خاندان
کی تصویریں دیکھیں۔
ہمیں اندازہ ہونا شروع ہوا کہ کتنے
ہمارے نزدیکی اور دور کے رشتہ داروں کے بچے پیدائشی ہی
بیماریوں میں مبتلا ہیں، بہت سے معذور ہیں،
کچھ پیدائش کے فوراً بعد فوت ہو گئے۔

I thought of my auntie in India.
She had been married
to a distant relative.
Their four daughters were fine.
But each of her four sons
were disabled from birth.
Then I thought of my own sister.
She had died at the age of thirty-two,
with a body like
a seven-year old child.
Then I looked at the photo
of my other sister.
Her son has needed
a wheelchair
since the age of eight.

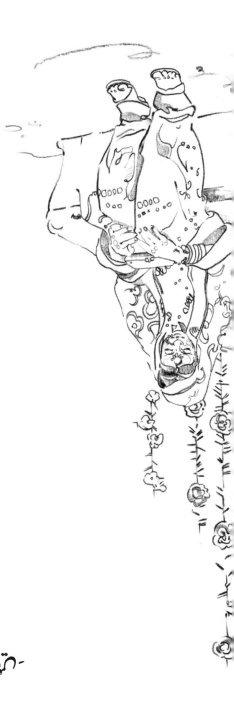

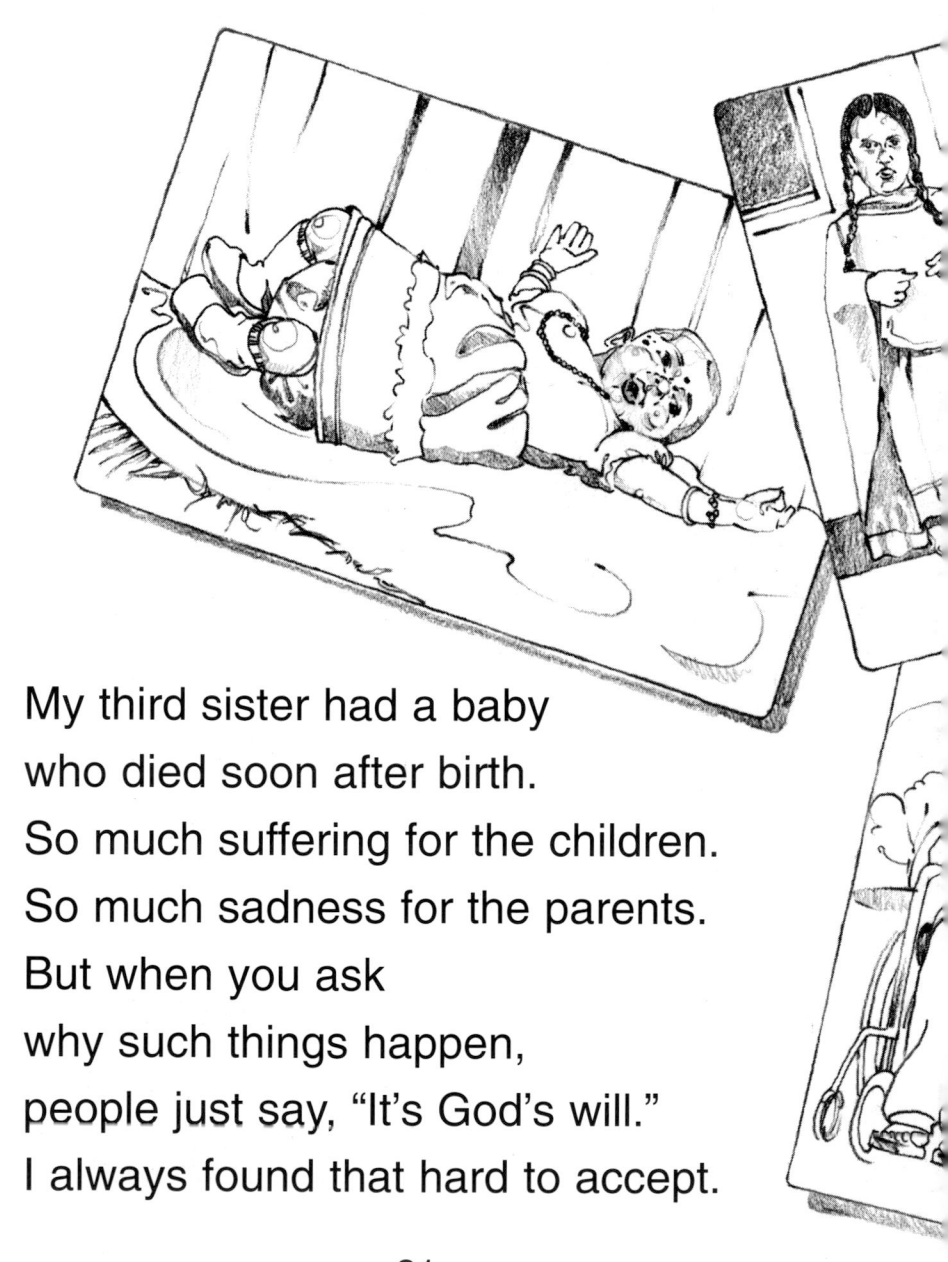

My third sister had a baby
who died soon after birth.
So much suffering for the children.
So much sadness for the parents.
But when you ask
why such things happen,
people just say, "It's God's will."
I always found that hard to accept.

میری تیسری بہن کی بے بی
پیدائش کے فوراً بعد فوت ہو گئی۔
بچوں کیلئے انتہائی تکلیف دہ۔
والدین کیلئے انتہائی دردناک۔
لیکن جب آپ اُن سے پوچھیں
کہ ایسی چیزیں کیوں ہوتی ہیں،
لوگ صرف یہ کہتے ہیں "خدا کی مرضی"۔
مجھے ہمیشہ یہ قبول کرنا مشکل لگا ہے۔

22

So later that week, I phoned my mother
and I explained this to her.
I said to her, "Many families see
having a disabled child
in a superstitious way. They think they
are being punished by God.
Or else they think the child was bad
in a past life.

اس ہفتے کچھ دیر بعد میں نے اپنی والدہ کو فون کیا
اور انہیں سمجھایا۔
اکثر خاندانوں میں معذور بچہ
توہم پرستی کا شکار ہے۔ وہ سمجھتے ہیں کہ
یہ اپاہج پن ان کیلئے خدا کی طرف سے سزا ہے
یا پھر وہ یہ سمجھتے ہیں کہ یہ بچہ
اپنی پچھلی زندگی میں برا تھا۔

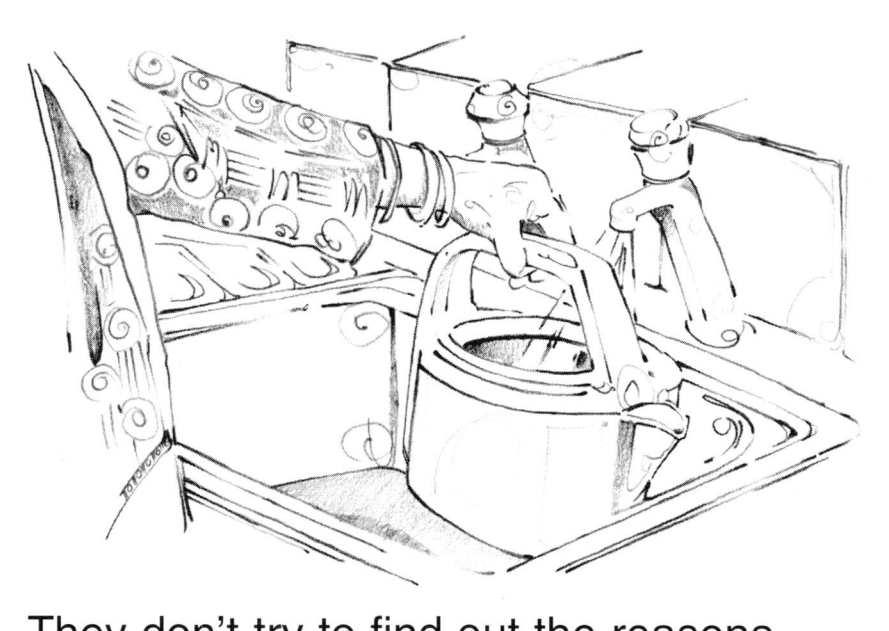

They don't try to find out the reasons
why things happen.
Sometimes, people justify customs
in an unthinking way.
Ask them why they do something
and they will say that they do it because
it has always been done that way!
They are scared of change,
even if the change
brings something better."

وہ وہ باتیں ڈھونڈنے کی کوشش نہیں کرتے

کہ یہ چیزیں کیوں ہوتی ہیں ۔

بعض دفعہ لوگ بغیر سوچے سمجھے

اپنے رسم و رواج کا جواز پیش کرتے ہیں ۔

اگر آپ اُن سے پوچھیں کہ آپ یہ کیوں کرتے ہیں

تو وہ کہتے ہیں ، وہ اس لئے ایسا کرتے ہیں

کیونکہ ہمیشہ سے ایسے ہوتا رہا ہے ۔

وہ تبدیلی سے خوفزدہ ہیں ۔

خواہ تبدیلی بہتر چیز لائے ۔

26

So, I am not saying a person
should never marry their cousin.
But if people want to do this,
they should each get tested first.
Because would anyone want to watch
their children suffer?
This has happened in our family.

یقیناً میں یہ نہیں کہ رہی کہ کوئی
اپنی کزنوں سے کبھی شادی نہ کرے
لیکن اگر لوگ ایسا کرنا چاہیں
تو پہلے اپنا ٹیسٹ کروالیں ۔
کیونکہ کون چاہتا ہے کہ وہ
اپنے بچوں کو تکلیف میں دیکھیں ۔
یہ ہمارے خاندان میں ہوا ہے ۔

28

I would like to see people learning
from our experience.
For me, this is the meaning
of education,
the purpose of learning
to read and write.
To learn about things that matter,
to make the world better.